Earthquakes

Kathy Galashan

Published in association with The Basic Skills Agency

Hodder & Stoughton

A MEMBER OF THE HODDER HEADLINE GROUP

Acknowledgements

Cover: Environmental Images

Photos: p3 FLPA/Mex; pp7, 11, 21 Popperfoto/Reuter; p16 Mary Evans Picture Library; p18 Popperfoto

Every effort has been made to trace copyright holders of material reproduced in this book. Any rights not acknowledged will be acknowledged in subsequent printings if notice is given to the publisher.

Orders; please contact Bookpoint Ltd, 39 Milton Park, Abingdon, Oxon OX14 4TD. Telephone: (44) 01235 400414, Fax: (44) 01235 400454. Lines are open from 9.00–6.00, Monday to Saturday, with a 24 hour message answering service.
Email address: orders@bookpoint.co.uk

British Library Cataloguing in Publication Data
A catalogue record for this title is available from the British Library

ISBN 0 340 77517 3

First published 2000
Impression number   10 9 8 7 6 5 4 3 2 1
Year   2005 2004 2003 2002 2001 2000

Copyright © 2000 Kathy Galashan

Typeset by GreenGate Publishing Services, Tonbridge, Kent.
Printed in Great Britain for Hodder and Stoughton Educational, a division of Hodder Headline Plc, 338 Euston Road, London NW1 3BH, by Redwood Books, Trowbridge, Wilts

Contents

We don't think about the ground.
Every day we walk and travel on it.
The pavement, the grass,
the floor of the house
are all there under our feet.

Then suddenly the ground moves and shakes.
It cracks open.
Nobody can stop it.
Nowhere is safe.

If you can't believe
in the ground under your feet,
what can you believe in?

An earthquake is one of the scariest things
in the world.

An Earthquake

Place: Mexico City
Date: 19 September 1985
Time: 7.18 am.

It was morning in Mexico City.
People were getting ready for the day.
The sun was shining
and the roads were getting busy.
People were on their way to work.

The ground began to shake.
The ground moved and cracked.
The roads moved
and waves of road appeared.
Cars bounced up and down.
Buses turned upside down.

Mexico City 1985

Inside flats and houses
cups, books and chairs
flew around rooms.
Cupboards fell over.
Glass smashed.

Tall buildings crashed down.
Concrete, glass and stone
rained down on to the pavement.
It sounded like a bomb.
The noise was tremendous.

Panic.
Where to go?
What to do?

The shaking seemed like hours,
but it was only a few minutes.

In those few minutes
thousands were dead.
Some were killed
by falling slabs of concrete
and broken glass.
The city centre was one big building site.

Thousands more were trapped
under collapsed buildings.
Many people were screaming and crying
and looking for their family, friends and pets.

This is how it was in Mexico City in 1985.
10,000 people died.
30,000 people were injured.
50,000 people were homeless.

After an Earthquake

Place: Armenia, Columbia, in South America
Date: 25 January 1999

922 people died.
3,600 people were hurt.
200,000 people lost their homes.

Everything was gone.
No food, no water, no gas or electricity.
Roads and trains were destroyed.
It was very hard to rescue people.

A member of the Red Cross tries to find survivors in a home
that was smashed after the earthquake. Colombia 1999

Special teams came from all over the world
with special equipment to help find people.
Some people were dug out
after eight or nine days.
They found babies still alive
but they couldn't find their parents.

Rescue work was very hard.
There was no electricity and there were no roads.
They could dig people out
but it was risky.
Maybe more bricks and rubbish
would fall down.

Sewers were cracked
and there was filthy water everywhere.
Gas pipes cracked and fires started
but there was no water to put them out.

People were starving.
They needed 150 tons of food a day
to feed everyone.
Some food came – but not enough.
It was difficult to get to the people
who needed food.

The army came to keep order.
They stopped people stealing
from smashed shops and houses.

After an earthquake everything is difficult.
It is hard to find food to eat and water to drink.
Keeping warm, keeping clean, and
going to the toilet become problems.

Some people lost their families.
Maybe they were alive,
maybe they were dead.
It was hard to find them.

It was difficult to bury people who died.
There were no coffins.
People were buried in plastic bags.

A homeless child in front of the ruins of his home. Colombia 1999

And then, after the big shock,
the ground moved again and again.
There were 30 aftershocks
in the following weeks.

Each aftershock was like a small earthquake.
When people felt the ground move again
they felt the terror of the main quake.
People were in panic.
Maybe there would be another big earthquake.

Landslides

Place: Yungay, Peru, in South America
Date: 31 May 1970

In Peru an enormous chunk of ice
fell off a mountain
because of an earthquake.
The ice melted
and became a river of mud
80 metres high.
The mud and rock raced down
the valley at 260 miles per hour,
faster than a racing car.

In the town
there was a loud crashing sound.
Three minutes later
the mud and rock swept away buildings
and covered the ruins.
The town of Yungay was gone.
Everybody was dead –
except for a few
who climbed up a little hill
in the middle of the town.

66,000 people died.

Giant Waves – Tsunamis

At sea, an earthquake can make
enormous waves.
In the ocean the waves can move
at 400 miles per hour,
faster than a jet plane.
When they hit land
they become giant waves.
They can be 25 metres high,
as high as a three-storey house.
The water crashes onto the land
smashing buildings and drowning people.

A Japanese print of a sailing vessel hit by a tidal wave
following an earthquake.

The water can travel
as much as half a mile inland.
Then the wall of water
rushes back out to sea,
dragging people, animals
and buildings with it.

In 1964 there was a tsunami warning
in San Francisco.
10,000 people went down to the sea
to watch the tsunami coming.
They thought it was exciting.

They saw it coming
but some couldn't escape.
They died.

Can we Prepare for an Earthquake?

In Tokyo on 1st September 1923
there was an earthquake.
Half the brick buildings fell down.
Wooden buildings burned down.
At least 575,000 homes were destroyed.
Fire raced through the city
and many people died in the flames.

Tokyo in ruins, 1923

This was the day the new Imperial Hotel
was going to open.
It was built to be safe in an earthquake.
It didn't fall down.
It was one of the few buildings left standing.

The new city of Tokyo was built
to be safe in an earthquake.

Buildings are low and strong.
Ten days' supply of water is kept
in earthquake-proof tanks.

There are stores of food and blankets.
Gas pipes and electricity cables
are protected.
So are roads and railways.

People can practise what to do
in an earthquake.
Police, hospitals and fire services
practise what to do.
In places where earthquakes may happen
children have lessons in school
on what to do
in an earthquake.

It's important to stay calm.
Many people get hurt because they panic.
They fall downstairs,
jump out of windows
or bang their heads.

Rescue services at work

It is often safer to stay inside.
A door frame is a good place to stand under.
This is one of the strongest parts
of a building.

In school, children can sit under desks.
If the ceiling falls down they are protected.

Before rescuing others
or leaving the building,
always put on shoes.
If you can, grab a torch.
There may be glass and rubbish
on the ground.

Don't use lifts.
They may get stuck
if the electricity supply gets cut off.

It is not possible to stop an earthquake
but we can be better prepared.

Earthquake Facts

Did you know?

In July 1201, about 1.1 million people
died in an earthquake
in the Near East, around the Mediterranean.

In London, on 6 April 1580
a young man called Thomas Grey
died in an earthquake.
He was killed by a brick.
Another woman, Muriel Everett,
died four days after the event.
They are the only people to die
from earthquakes in Britain.

In 1775 there was a great earthquake
in Lisbon in Portugal.
It was All Saints Day.
The churches were crowded.
The walls cracked and people inside died.
Altogether about 60,000 people died.
Some were drowned by a giant wave.
Some died in fires.

In Alaska in 1964 an earthquake and tsunami
caused about $750 million of damage.

In December 1989 there was an earthquake
in New South Wales in Australia.
12 people died.
120 were injured.
It was the first time anyone had died
in an earthquake in Australia.

In 1990 a man was rescued
from under a hotel in The Phillipines.
He had been there for 14 days.

On Tuesday 15 August, 1999
there was a major earthquake
in Izmit, Turkey.
The first shock lasted 45 seconds
and in that time
the ground moved eight feet.
Twenty million people felt the earthquake
and heard the roar of rocks moving.

Oil refineries were set alight.
Buildings collapsed like packs of cards.
Television pictures brought
the horror of the earthquake
to homes around the world.

Over 16,000 people died.
There were some miracles.
A four-year-old boy, Ismail Cimen,
was pulled out alive after six days
under rubble.
His uncle was sure he had died
with others in the family.
His grave was already dug
and then he was found.

After the earthquake in Izmit, Turkey

The highest number of deaths
in the last hundred years
was in Tangshen, China.
The number of people
reported dead was 750,000.
Later, the Chinese government
said 242,000 people had died.

In Parkway, California, there is an earthquake
about every 20 years.

In the last 100 years, on average,
about 15,000 people have died EVERY YEAR
from earthquakes.

Did you know?

You can feel, hear and see
what an earthquake is like
at the Natural History Museum in London.